IF LOST, PLEASE BE KIND
AND RETURN TO:

D1202830

# CONTENTS

*This book is dedicated to you, for picking it up and taking the time
to do something for YOU. When you take time to care for yourself,
you can also be a better self for everyone else in your life.*

# INTRODUCTION

If you're experiencing feelings of stress and anxiety on a daily basis, you are not alone. Our busy schedules can pile pressure on us to find time and solutions that improve our own well-being, creating an endless cycle of overwhelm.

We have thoughtfully designed this book, so you can relax and unwind through the art of coloring. It also provides you with simple tools and techniques to guide you through stressful phases or situations that promote anxiety. These tools can help you to feel more in control over how you choose to respond to your feelings and emotions.

*Unwind Yourself* is filled with beautifully-curated designs to help you relax and calm down. Each illustration is paired with a simple cue containing a beneficial daily mindfulness practice, practical tip for better health and vitality, or positive attitude prompt. For deeper insights into each topic, we have also included a Bonus Content section at the end of the book, which provides additional information on the various tools & techniques, and how they can be used to nurture your body, mind and spirit.

You can use as little or as much color as you like. We have purposefully designed a combination of simple and more complex illustrations worthy of wall display.

Time is a precious resource, and we understand that having hours with which to color may be a luxury. The simple designs are easy to complete, giving you a great sense of satisfaction and achievement. You may decide to do the more complex designs in one sitting, or leave space to come back to them another time.

Get creative with the coloring medium you use—pencils, markers, pastels, gel pens, etc. However, we don't recommend the use of water-based paints on this paper. At the end of the book, you'll find a pen-test page, where it's safe to sample your choice of coloring medium. Be proud of your works of art and display them around your home! The perforations make it easy to remove the pages from the book.

# GETTING STARTED

1. Treat the coloring experience like a mindfulness practice. Find a quiet, relaxing space to set yourself up, so you can focus.
2. Decide on a design or technique that resonates with how you are feeling in the moment.
3. Let go! Let your creativity flow, and just do what feels good.
4. After you've added your personal coloring touch to the page, take a moment to reflect on how the practice made you feel.
5. Most importantly, we wish you a calming and relaxing coloring experience.

# JUST BREATHE

It's alright if all you do today is inhale and exhale.

Become aware of the present moment.

Remember, you are safe, you are supported,
and you are at peace.

# BACK TO BASICS

Relaxing with a hot cup of tea is a
ritual that always does a world of good.

A traditional herbal tea blend with
chamomile and/or lavender can help to release
stress and anxiety and soothe the mind.

# SLEEP SOUNDLY

Train your body to fall asleep more quickly
and wake up feeling more refreshed.

By going to bed at the same time each night and
getting up at the same time in the morning, you set
the stage for your body to establish a sleep rhythm.
The result is a more regular sleep pattern that
makes it easier to fall asleep and wake up.

# NOURISH YOURSELF

When you eat, consider whether the foods
you choose will nourish your body—
treat what you eat as a lifestyle, not a diet.

# TAKE TIME OUT

Release yourself from a situation that makes
you feel overwhelmed by taking time out to reset.

You might simply step away to
grab a glass of water or go for a walk.

# PUMP IT

Exercising regularly can help you on multiple levels—
it can reduce stress, improve mood, and boost energy.

It also allows your mind to go "offline" for a while,
which is beneficial when you're feeling overwhelmed.

# SPEND TIME
# IN NATURE

Take yourself to your favorite outdoor place,
where you feel most comfortable with nature,
and simply absorb what you see.

# A QUIET MIND

Try a meditation practice to bring your
mind's attention to the present moment.

By focusing on the here and now, you can let go
of stress and anxiety about the past or future.

# WRITE YOUR EMOTIONS

Release negative thoughts from your mind by putting your emotions and feelings down on paper. Just write whatever comes to mind, without censoring yourself.

Let the words flow.

# IDENTIFY YOUR TRIGGERS

Reflect on situations that make
you feel anxious and stressed.

Ask yourself what might be causing
those feelings and look for patterns.

# LIFE IS A BALANCE

Bring your body and mind back into
a state of balance.

Take up yoga, Qi Gong, and tai chi and combine
rhythmic breathing with light stretches, gentle
postures, and flowing movements.

# PLAYTIME

Playtime is crucial for your mental
and physical well-being at any age.

So go ahead and give yourself permission
to unwind and have some fun.

# REPEAT AFTER ME

In a challenging moment, repeat a phrase that is meaningful to you. You could say something as simple as "I can do this" or recite a spiritual mantra.

Remember, you are in control of your thoughts and how you react to stressful situations.

Choose to focus on what is positive and calming.

# BREAK THE PATTERN

Be honest with yourself and identify habits
you have fallen into that aren't serving you.

These behaviors can often start out with good
intentions—like working long hours to meet
a deadline—but if they become the norm, they
can have negative long-term impacts on
your health and well-being.

# LAUGHTER IS THE
# BEST MEDICINE

Visualize your favorite humorous moments
and laugh out loud.

Positive emotions can quickly pick up your mood
and help you feel more joyful and lighthearted.

# PUT A LABEL ON IT

Labeling a physical sensation or emotion
you are feeling may help you step away from it.

Simply by identifying and acknowledging
it, you can allow the feeling to pass.

# TAKE YOURSELF TO ANOTHER PLACE

Visualize tranquil locations or experiences
in your mind that help you relax and focus.

Visualization lets you bring a piece of
paradise with you wherever you go.

# TALK TO SOMEONE YOU TRUST

It's important to remember that someone will always listen, and you are never alone. Reach out to a close friend, family member, partner, therapist, or even a hotline.

Sometimes simply being heard is comfort enough and will ease your pain.

# LISTEN TO NATURE

Ditch the headphones!

Take a break from your hectic day, tune in,
and listen to the calming sounds of nature.

Nature's music soothes the soul.

# RECHARGE YOURSELF

Self-care is essential and should
never leave you feeling guilty!

Taking time to focus on your own needs
allows you to show up better, not only for
yourself, but for everyone else in your life.

# LET GO OF PERFECTION

You'll never fit into a perfect circle, which
is what makes you human, my friend.

Embrace mistakes instead of being fearful of them.

# BODY SCAN

Try a body scan to boost awareness of your
mind-body connection.

By focusing your attention on each part of your
body, you can release tension and ease anxiety.

# CULTIVATE A
# POSITIVE ATTITUDE

Surround yourself with people who
make you feel great about yourself!

Positive people will help you stay upbeat,
even when things aren't going your way.

So seek out the company of supportive people.

# LEARN
# SOMETHING NEW

Pick a topic or hobby that interests you, dive
in, and commit to learning more about it.

# FOLLOW YOUR SENSES

Be present and acknowledge your surroundings.

Absorb positive feelings by working
your way through your senses to find
something that really connects with you.

# BE KIND TO YOURSELF

You will never speak to anyone more than
you speak to yourself in your own head.

The words and tone you use can affect
your mood and how you see yourself.

# I WILL GET
# THROUGH THIS

Even in your darkest moments,
you can choose to rise into the light.

Challenges and obstacles may arise at
any time, and on some days it might seem
like the darkness is winning.

You have it within you to get through
whatever is standing in your way, and the
light always shines at the end of every tunnel.

# SEEK HELP

Healing comes in many different forms.

If you feel like you need more support, consider finding a professional who will best suit your needs.

Find someone who can help you think through your options and come up with different approaches.

# MIRROR, MIRROR ON THE WALL

When you look into the mirror, who do you see looking back at you? Is this person equipped with the tools and techniques to overcome situations of anxiety and stress?

Draw an image that represents how you want to live your life. You might be pleasantly surprised how far you have already come.

# JUST BREATHE

*It's alright if all you do today is inhale and exhale. Become aware of the present moment. Remember, you are safe, you are supported, and you are at peace.*

Taking long, purposeful breaths triggers the body's relaxation response and gently disengages your mind from thoughts and sensations that don't serve you.

To get started, find yourself a quiet, calm environment where you can comfortably sit or lie down. Close your eyes and envision the way a sleeping baby peacefully breathes. Its breaths are deep, and its belly naturally rises up and down with ease. Breathe in gently through your nose, feeling the breath enter deep into your stomach. Breathe out naturally through your mouth. Repeat five times or as long as you feel you need to feel more relaxed.

# BACK TO BASICS

*Relaxing with a hot cup of tea is a ritual that always does a world of good. A traditional herbal tea blend with chamomile and/or lavender can help to release stress and anxiety and soothe the mind.*

Herbal teas are a centuries-old tradition used to help restore balance and calm minds. You can enjoy these beverages without worrying about your caffeine intake, as they are made from all types of dried flowers, fruits, spices, and herbs.

With such a variety of herbal flavors, you can surely find something that suits your taste buds. Also, many of these teas have beneficial health properties like antioxidants or anti-inflammatory agents.

# SLEEP SOUNDLY

*Train your body to fall asleep more quickly and wake up feeling more refreshed. By going to bed at the same time each night and getting up at the same time in the morning, you set the stage for your body to establish a sleep rhythm. The result is a more regular sleep pattern that makes it easier to fall asleep and wake up.*

To function at your best, you need to get enough sleep. Aim for 7.5 hours of sleep each night and create a consistent routine. Put a reminder in your calendar or set an alarm to not only wake up, but also to prompt you to get ready for bed.

Your body will get used to your sleeping times, and it will become easier for you to fall and stay asleep. In addition, using guided meditation may help your restless mind to gently drift off to sleep when you first start your new routine. Remember to also keep digital devices out of reach in your bedroom.

## NOURISH YOURSELF

*When you eat, consider whether the foods you choose will nourish your body—treat what you eat as a lifestyle, not a diet.*

You know that balancing nutrition and nourishing your body is essential, but the temptations of convenience and enjoyment can get in the way. Take the emotion out of eating by treating it with a "food is fuel" mentality. Make your food choices based on nutritional value, ingredient quality, and how your body feels after you eat.

To start your lifestyle change, add more before you take anything away. Yes, that's right—get into the habit of eating more of what your body needs before taking away what it doesn't. Plan ahead and prioritize well-balanced meals with lots of vegetables. Keep healthy snacks on hand to avoid impulse eating. Most importantly, limit sugars, processed foods, and alcohol. When treating yourself, eat slowly, without distractions, so you can really enjoy the food's flavors and textures and consume only a single portion.

## TAKE TIME OUT

*Release yourself from a situation that makes you feel overwhelmed by taking time out to reset. You might simply step away to grab a glass of water or go for a walk.*

Remember that taking time out for yourself isn't selfish; it's essential. When you give yourself a break, you can come back to your responsibilities feeling refreshed and ready to take on the world. Distance often gives you a fresh perspective.

Since life frequently feels like a never-ending stream of deadlines and appointments, try to plan your week ahead, blocking out time in your diary to take a breather and clear your head. Maybe you could go outside for a walk in the fresh air during your lunch break or book a massage to let yourself unwind. Your mind and body will thank you for it.

## PUMP IT

*Exercising regularly can help you on multiple levels—it can reduce stress, improve mood, and boost energy. It also allows your mind to go "offline" for a while, which is beneficial when you're feeling overwhelmed.*

Start at your own pace. If you're new to exercise, even taking a short 20-minute walk a few times a week or hitting a goal of 10,000 steps throughout the day is great progress. If you love to exercise but time is a limiting factor, prioritize 10 minutes and try a high-intensity interval training (HIIT) workout from home. Loads of apps are available to get you started.

## SPEND TIME IN NATURE

*Take yourself to your favorite outdoor place, where you feel most comfortable with nature, and simply absorb what you see.*

Take off your shoes and feel the grass or sand between your toes. Embrace the warm sun on your face and feel the breeze on your skin. Listen to the sounds of water or birds. Soak it up and embrace your inner mother nature.

## A QUIET MIND

*Try a meditation practice to bring your mind's attention to the present moment. By focusing on the here and now, you can let go of stress and anxiety about the past or future.*

Meditation is an effective way to shift your awareness into the present and improve concentration. By taking a few minutes each day to sit quietly and focus on your breath, you can learn to control your thoughts and emotions and ultimately reduce physical stress.

To get started, find a comfortable position, close your eyes, and breathe in slowly and deeply. Then exhale slowly. Pay attention to the sensation of your breath entering and leaving your body. If your mind wanders, simply refocus on your breath. Many guided meditations are available online—they're a great way to get comfortable with this practice.

## WRITE YOUR EMOTIONS

*Release negative thoughts from your mind by putting your emotions and feelings down on paper. Just write whatever comes to mind, without censoring yourself. Let the words flow.*

The most important thing is that you're letting yourself express what's inside you. As you write, you can create a fresh perspective, work through difficult situations, and/or process complicated emotions. Writing allows you to vent your frustrations without worrying about anyone's opinion.

# IDENTIFY YOUR TRIGGERS

*Reflect on situations that make you feel anxious and stressed. Ask yourself what might be causing those feelings and look for patterns.*

Identifying your triggers is an essential step in managing your anxiety. Once you know what they are, you can take steps to avoid or better deal with your triggers, which can help you feel more in control and less anxious overall.

A good approach is to keep a journal of your anxiety experiences. Make notes when you feel anxious: What were you doing at the time? What might have prompted those feelings? Over time, you'll likely see patterns emerge, which can help you identify your triggers and take steps to manage them more effectively.

# LIFE IS A BALANCE

*Bring your body and mind back into a state of balance.*

*Take up yoga, Qi Gong, and tai chi and combine rhythmic breathing with light stretches, gentle postures, and flowing movements.*

People have practiced these ancient relaxation methods for centuries, and they have proven incredibly effective at reducing stress and promoting well-being.

Yoga is a great way to relax your mind and body while also getting some exercise. Qi Gong is perfect for those who want to focus on their breathing and slow down their minds. Tai chi is a wonderful way to get your body moving and promote balance and coordination. Try finding a local studio near you that offers these classes. Or, if you feel nervous about starting out, try it online in the comfort of your home.

# PLAYTIME

*Playtime is crucial for your mental and physical well-being at any age. So go ahead and give yourself permission to unwind and have some fun.*

Your brain and body listen to what you tell them through your activity. If you constantly focus on work and stress, they'll believe that's all life offers. But if you take some time out for play, you send the message that there's more to life—it's about joy, too.

Playtime is also a great way to connect with others and build relationships. Your kids will love it if you suddenly skate or ride a bike with them! Play can take the form of exercise as well, such as participating in a team sport or a dance class.

## REPEAT AFTER ME

*In a challenging moment, repeat a phrase that is meaningful to you. You could say something as simple as "I can do this" or recite a spiritual mantra. Remember, you are in control of your thoughts and how you react to stressful situations. Choose to focus on what is positive and calming.*

A mantra is a word or phrase you can repeat aloud or silently. You can chant or simply speak it with the intention of refocusing and stilling your thoughts. Mantras are perfect little tools to have up your sleeve, particularly in situations where you're unable to remove yourself from your current environment—like when you're in a work meeting or stuck in traffic.

The key is to pick a mantra that resonates with you on a personal level. By taking a few moments to focus on your breath and repeat your mantra, you can create a still, peaceful place in the midst of stress. In doing so, you'll tap into a strong, calm inner reserve that will help you get through whatever challenges you face.

## BREAK THE PATTERN

*Be honest with yourself and identify habits you have fallen into that aren't serving you. These behaviors can often start out with good intentions—like working long hours to meet a deadline—but if they become the norm, they can have negative long-term impacts on your health and well-being.*

Whatever the disempowering habit may be, it's important to break the cycle. If you can recognize destructive behaviors like skipping meals, drinking too much caffeine or alcohol, or constantly checking your phone, then you have already taken the first step.

Always remember that you're in control of your own decisions, and you have the power within you to make better choices. Consider using a habit tracker to help you eliminate your negative, disempowering habits and establish and maintain positive, empowering habits in your daily routine. Start slowly, and concentrate on the one or two habits that will have the biggest impact on your health.

## LAUGHTER IS THE BEST MEDICINE

*Visualize your favorite humorous moments and laugh out loud.*

*Positive emotions can quickly pick up your mood and help you feel more joyful and lighthearted.*

It may sound silly, but it's true ... laughter helps lower stress hormones like cortisol and increase feel-good hormones like endorphins. It can also improve blood flow and relax your muscles, and all these benefits can reduce stress.

So, next time you're feeling stressed, go through the photos or videos on your phone and pull out some fun memories you've saved. Or, try watching your favorite funny TV show or movie. You could even read a humorous book or comic strip. Whatever makes you laugh, do more of it!

## PUT A LABEL ON IT

*Labeling a physical sensation or emotion you are feeling may help you step away from it. Simply by identifying and acknowledging it, you can allow the feeling to pass.*

Emotions can be intense and overwhelming, but they are often less daunting when you put a label on them. By identifying the emotion, you create awareness that allows you to disconnect from it.

Have you ever seen a computer game where the character receives a prize or token that pops up above their head and then disappears in a little puff of smoke? Labeling your emotions like a game can be a light-hearted approach that reminds you to be present with your feelings. Try to physically see words like "frustrated," "angry," "sad," and "lonely" light up in your mind, and then let them disappear before your eyes.

## TAKE YOURSELF TO ANOTHER PLACE

*Visualize tranquil locations or experiences in your mind that help you relax and focus. Visualization lets you bring a piece of paradise with you wherever you go.*

Give yourself a break from thinking about all the things you have to do or places you have to be. Take yourself to a calmer place, and allow your stress to melt away. This mental escape can be a memory of a happy time or place, or it can be a made-up location you find relaxing. Wherever you choose to go, make sure it makes you feel at ease.

Once you've found your happy place, close your eyes and imagine the sights, sounds, and smells around you. The more details you can see and feel in your happy place, the better. When you're ready, open your eyes and come back to the present moment, feeling refreshed and rejuvenated.

## TALK TO SOMEONE YOU TRUST

*It's important to remember that someone will always listen, and you are never alone. Reach out to a close friend, family member, partner, therapist, or even a hotline. Sometimes simply being heard is comfort enough and will ease your pain.*

Speaking your mind aloud gives you the opportunity to process your thoughts and articulate your feelings from another perspective. Just talking about what's causing you stress or anxiety can be incredibly helpful, as it tends to release the negative tension from your body. It can also allow you to see the situation more clearly and come up with a plan to deal with it.

## LISTEN TO NATURE

*Ditch the headphones! Take a break from your hectic day, tune in, and listen to the calming sounds of nature. Nature's music soothes the soul.*

When you need to relax, nothing helps like tuning in to the sounds of nature. Whether it's the trickle of a creek, the gentle rhythm of waves against the shore, or the birds singing in the trees, listening to these natural soundscapes can help you feel calm and at ease. So, the next time you feel stressed, take a break and listen to nature's music. It's certain to pacify your spirit.

## RECHARGE YOURSELF

*Self-care is essential and should never leave you feeling guilty! Taking time to focus on your own needs allows you to show up better, not only for yourself, but for everyone else in your life.*

Choose a self-care activity that's right for you. The important thing is to exercise self-care in the way that serves you best and allows you to switch off and let the stress drain out of your body. For some, self-care can look like a bubble bath, a massage, or curling up with a good book. For others, it may be getting your hands dirty in the garden, decluttering your room, or generally tidying up. The great thing is, there is no right or wrong way to practice self-care. Just make it your own.

## LET GO OF PERFECTION

*You'll never fit into a perfect circle, which is what makes you human, my friend. Embrace mistakes instead of being fearful of them.*

If you're constantly striving for perfection, you'll never be satisfied, which doesn't mean you should lower your standards. You have the blessing and freedom to explore life with all its twists and turns, so you will inevitably make mistakes and develop flaws. Instead of beating yourself up, try to see your blunders as opportunities to learn and grow. When faced with similar situations in the future, you'll be able to approach them differently and do better.

Human beings are often primed from an early age to get everything right and avoid mishaps. In many cases, this expectation comes from a place of love and protection—from our parents. However, it can lead to missing out on valuable life lessons. When you fail, you learn resilience, responsibility, and how to rethink your approach and strategies for yourself. These opportunities make your life unique and rich.

## BODY SCAN

*Try a body scan to boost awareness of your mind-body connection. By focusing your attention on each part of your body, you can release tension and ease anxiety.*

Body scanning is a simple, yet effective way to learn how to relax. It is a form of mindfulness meditation that helps you focus on your breath and become aware of your body's sensations without judgment or the intention to change anything.

Start by finding a comfortable place to sit or lie down. Close your eyes and focus on your breath. Breathe in and out slowly and deeply. Mentally scan your body, starting at the top of your head and working your way down to your toes. Focus on each part and pay attention to any areas of pain or discomfort. Don't try to change anything, just notice what you feel. When you reach your toes, take a few deep breaths and slowly open your eyes.

## CULTIVATE A POSITIVE ATTITUDE

*Surround yourself with people who make you feel great about yourself! Positive people will help you stay upbeat, even when things aren't going your way. So seek out the company of supportive people.*

Have you ever noticed that you tend to adopt the behaviors and attitudes of the people closest to you? We're all highly influenced by the people with whom we spend the most time. Therefore, it's vital to surround yourself with positive people who lift you up, keep you motivated, and help you reach your potential. When you're mindful of the company you keep, you can shift your worldview and purposefully focus on relationships that lead to fulfillment and happiness.

Surrounding yourself with like-minded people doesn't mean cutting out everyone who isn't perfectly positive all the time. However, reflecting on current relationships and being more intentional about the relationships you cultivate can ensure that most people in your life are supportive and encouraging.

## LEARN SOMETHING NEW

*Pick a topic or hobby that interests you, dive in, and commit to learning more about it.*

Learning something new can be a great way to relax and relieve anxiety. Choosing a topic that interests you may be an enjoyable and invigorating way to divert your attention away from negative ideas and concerns. It can also encourage you to feel more confident and capable. When you have skills and know how to do something, you can feel more confident and in control of your life.

You can learn so many things—a new language, how to play an instrument, or how to cook a new dish, for starters. The possibilities are endless, and it just might be the key to helping you feel better.

## FOLLOW YOUR SENSES

*Be present and acknowledge your surroundings. Absorb positive feelings by working your way through your senses to find something that really connects with you.*

During a moment of overwhelm, it can be tricky to find the right tool to calm your nerves. Try drawing upon your senses to narrow down your focus. Start by slowly looking around your environment for something pleasing, or tune in to a specific sound in the distance. One sense is likely to stand out more than the others and spark an idea that will lead you toward feeling better.

During this sensory scan, try hugging or holding onto a soft cushion if touching something brought you comfort. If a scent was calming, try to savor the smell, breathing it in deeply through your nose with your eyes closed. The goal is to use your senses to find something that grounds you in the present moment. Once you've found that, it can be much easier to move forward and calm your nerves.

## BE KIND TO YOURSELF

*You will never speak to anyone more than you speak to yourself in your own head. The words and tone you use can affect your mood and how you see yourself.*

Speak kindly to yourself; it can make a world of difference. When you make a mistake, it's okay to feel disappointed, but talk to yourself the way you would talk to a friend or a loved one in the same situation. Let go of self-judgment. Be patient with yourself; be understanding; be forgiving. By being kind to yourself, you can create a more positive outlook. When you're caring for yourself, you open up the possibility for happiness, success, and love. A little self-compassion can go a long way.

# I WILL GET THROUGH THIS

*Even in your darkest moments, you can choose to rise into the light. Challenges and obstacles may arise at any time, and on some days it might seem like the darkness is winning.*

*You have it within you to get through whatever is standing in your way, and the light always shines at the end of every tunnel.*

To help you step out of your overwhelm, write a list of your concerns, separating them into two columns: "In my control" and "Out of my control." Embrace your inner strength to tear the page into two and crumple the list of items that are not in your control. Throw it in the trash or even burn it in a safe environment to experience a physical sensation of letting go. Make peace with the past, and open your heart to new beginnings.

Come back to the list of items that are in your control and pick one item to take action on now. It might be a phone call or sending a message to a loved one with whom you are currently experiencing tension. Work your way through this list over the coming days or weeks to bring yourself back into the light.

# SEEK HELP

*Healing comes in many different forms. If you feel like you need more support, consider finding a professional who will best suit your needs.*

*Find someone who can help you think through your options and come up with different approaches.*

Acknowledging the need for further assistance could be one of the bravest things you ever do. Make a start within your comfort zone, and be open to different types of services and healing practices. Healing may be an ongoing journey; always stay true to yourself and know that you are worthy of a happy and fulfilling life.

Consider what service would serve you most. A massage therapist can promote physical stress relief by reducing muscle tension. A counselor can help you identify healthy coping mechanisms and constructively work through your challenges. A personal trainer can enhance your health and fitness with an exercise program, and a life coach can support you with your goals and dreams. Perhaps even a general check-up with your family doctor is a good place to start to explore your physical and mental needs and healing options.

# TEST YOUR PENS

Use the pattern on the right as a safe place to test all your pens, markers and colors. Don't hold back, this is an opportunity to use your imagination.

# tag us on Instagram

Lucky winners will get a free gift.

Simply tag us with your coloring page in use **@my.ryve**

---

## YOUR PURCHASE INCLUDES

---

### FREE GOAL SETTING PRINTABLES

Scan the QR Code with your cell phone camera or visit
www.myryve.com/templates

### FREE COLORING PAGE RE-PRINTS

Scan the QR Code with your cell phone camera or visit
www.myryve.com/unwindyourself

## A MEAL FOR A HOMELESS PERSON

For every product we sell, a homeless person receives a meal
www.myryve.com/giving